CANTATAS FOR SOLO VOICE

Recent Researches in the Music of the Baroque Era is one of four quarterly series (Middle Ages and Early Renaissance; Renaissance; Baroque Era; Classical Era) which make public the early music that is being brought to light in the course of current musicological research.

Each volume is devoted to works by a single composer or in a single genre of composition, chosen because of their potential interest to scholars and performers, and prepared for publication according to the standards that govern the making of all reliable historical editions.

Subscribers to this series, as well as patrons of subscribing institutions, are invited to apply for information about the "Copyright-Sharing Policy" of A-R Editions, Inc., under which the contents of this volume may be reproduced free of charge for performance use.

Correspondence should be addressed:

A-R Editions, Inc.
315 West Gorham Street
Madison, Wisconsin 53703

RECENT RESEARCHES IN THE MUSIC OF THE BAROQUE ERA • VOLUME XXXII

Antonio Vivaldi

CANTATAS FOR SOLO VOICE

Part I: Soprano

Edited by Meneve Dunham

A-R EDITIONS, INC. • MADISON

Copyright © 1979, A-R Editions, Inc.

ISSN 0484-0828

ISBN 0-89579-115-3 (Set, Parts I and II)
ISBN 0-89579-116-1 (Part I)

Library of Congress Cataloging in Publication Data:

Vivaldi, Antonio, 1678-1741.
    Cantatas : for solo voice.

    (Recent researches in the music of the baroque era ;
v. 32-33)
    Sparsely figured bass realized for keyboard instru-
ment.
    Edited from mss. in the Biblioteca nazionale di Torino
(Foà 27-28) and the Sächsische Landesbibliothek,
Dresden (Mus. 1/J/7)
    Includes bibliographical references.
    Italian texts with English translations: p. xvi.
    CONTENTS: pt. 1. Cantatas for soprano and continuo.
Cantatas for soprano, continuo, and obbligato instru-
ments.—pt. 2. Cantatas for alto and continuo. Cantatas
for alto, continuo, and obbligato instruments.
    1. Solo cantatas, Secular—Vocal scores with continuo.
2. Solo cantatas, Secular—Scores. I. Dunham, Meneve.
II. Series.
[M3.1] [M1611] [M1620].R238 vol. 32-33 780'.903'2s
ISBN 0-89579-115-3   [782.8'2'54]   79-4263

Contents

Part I

Cantatas for Soprano and Continuo

Cantatas for Soprano, Continuo, and Obbligato Instruments

Part II

Cantatas for Alto and Continuo

Cantatas for Alto, Continuo, and Obbligato Instruments

Preface

A Vivaldi renaissance occurred in the 1930s as a result of the uncovering of a large collection of manuscripts in the holdings of a Salesian college near Turin, Italy. With the transference of the volumes to the Biblioteca Nazionale di Torino, a major segment of the output of "il Prete rosso" could be examined and evaluated.

Since World War II, four biographical studies of substantial length have been completed,[1] and a complete edition of the composer's works has been undertaken by the Istituto Italiano Antonio Vivaldi in cooperation with Ricordi & Co. of Milan.[2] The emphasis of these scholarly works has been on Vivaldi's instrumental compositions.

Vivaldi wrote twenty-five cantatas for soprano; twenty-two of these have continuo accompaniment and three are accompanied by both continuo and obbligato instruments. His cantatas for the alto voice include six with continuo accompaniment and two others accompanied with continuo and obbligato instruments.

The present edition consists of two volumes. The volume of cantatas for the soprano voice (Part I) includes the three for voice and continuo with obbligato mentioned above and five others with only the continuo accompaniment. Sixteen other Vivaldi cantatas for soprano and continuo are also well worth preparing for a modern edition. The remaining cantata for soprano, *O mie porpore* (C/7),[3] lacks Vivaldi's careful attention to construction and detail. The volume of cantatas for the alto voice (Part II) contains all of the extant cantatas for this range, except *Qual in pioggia dorata i dolci rai* (C/9) which is of decidedly lesser musical quality.

Sources

The main corpus of Vivaldi's cantatas is contained in two volumes (Foà 27 and 28) held by the Biblioteca Nazionale di Torino.[4] The contents of these volumes are listed in Tables 1 and 2 on pp. viii-ix. Some twenty other volumes of the Foà collection contain Vivaldi operas, oratorios, motets, and arias. In addition, the Sächsische Landesbibliothek (Dresden) possesses one manuscript—Mus. 1/J/7—containing ten Vivaldi cantatas (given in Table 3 on p. x), five of which duplicate works in the Foà cantata volumes.[5]

Three other cantatas ascribed to Vivaldi appear in a Florentine manuscript bearing the title *Cantate di Diversi Autori di Secolo 17mo, Libro 2do.*[6] However, the motto technique so characteristic of Alessandro Scarlatti is used in the arias of these compositions, whereas Vivaldi's usual compositional technique in the works of the Turin and Dresden manuscripts does not involve immediate text repetition. It is therefore doubtful that these three cantatas are by Vivaldi, so they do not appear in the complete listing of cantatas in Tables 1, 2, and 3.

The alto setting of *Amor hai vinto* (C/10) appears in Foà 27 three times. (1) The cantata first appears in Vivaldi's hand in score form for all parts (C/10). (2) Later, after some 190 folios, Foà 27 contains the performing parts (also in Vivaldi's hand) for the accompanying three string instruments (C/10a); there, the word *"Rigore"* indicates the final word of the *recitativo secco*. (3) This section (C/10a) is followed immediately by a copyist's version of the same cantata (C/10b), which gives only the vocal line and continuo part (see Table 1).

In the score form of *Amor hai vinto* (C/10), the second recitative is set both as *secco* and *accompagnato*. The version with simple continuo accompaniment appears above a portion of the *accompagnato* setting (folios 56v-57r). Since the performing parts contain only the *accompagnato* version, this is the setting that appears in the edition; the *secco* setting is given as an alternative (see Part II, p. 94).

The information currently available indicates that thirty-three different cantatas written by Vivaldi are extant. Unfortunately, none of the cantata texts has been identified as belonging to any one poet. Remo Giazotto does quote one entry from a Roman diary in which the writer refers to Vivaldi arias with texts supplied by a Jesuit, Monsignor Barbieri, being performed at the Colonna home in Rome.[7] However, the manuscript copies of the cantatas in Turin and Dresden bear no inscriptions or dates that identify any of the texts as having been written by Barbieri.

In the Foà collection, a section of one cantata text (C/17) *Nel partir dà te mio caro* appears to have been written by Vivaldi as he was composing the musical setting. Although the recitative of this cantata is begun four times and only the last version is completed, Vivaldi partially underlays the texts in the three rejected versions, also.[8] Since *Nel partir dà te mio caro* is in Vivaldi's hand, he may possibly have written the text himself.[9]

TABLE 1
TABLE OF CONTENTS FOR FOÀ 27

a. There are two concurrent systems of pagination in each Foà volume. The more consistent one—the one that begins the numbering with the title-page and assigns a number to every *recto* page of each folio—is reflected in Tables 1 and 2. In these Tables a number refers to the *recto* side unless specified "v" *(verso)*.

b. The title (appearing in italics) is derived from the first line of the text.

c. To facilitate discussion of the compositions, a symbol (C/1, C/2, etc.) is assigned to each cantata. The cantatas are listed in the order in which they appear within each of the two Foà volumes and the Dresden manuscript (Mus. 1/J/7).

d. An asterisk before a cantata number in the Tables indicates those which appear in this edition.

The Cantatas

Just as the writer of each cantata text secures poetic unity by limiting the action to a single place and time, so the composer usually achieves musical unity in most cantatas by relating all the movements of a given cantata to one tonal center. Intermediary tonal levels (usually closely related keys) selected by Vivaldi for the purpose of contrast between movements reflect a typical baroque practice. Usually, related tonal levels are touched briefly during the movement. The cumulative result is a movement that is tonally unified within itself or becomes a modulation to the tonal level of the aria which follows.

A work is entitled "cantata" by Vivaldi when a composition for solo voice consists of two recitatives and two arias, or two arias separated by a rec-

TABLE 2
TABLE OF CONTENTS FOR FOÀ 28

Folio	Title	Number	Folio	Title	Number
1	Dj/ Don Antonio Vivaldi/ Cantate:/ Tomo II		41-175v	[Collection of arias]	
			176-176v	[Blank]	
2-12v	Cantata ad Alto Solo con Istrom^ti. Del Vivaldi *Cessate, omai cessate*	*C/12	177-180v	Cantata Del Vivaldi *Sorge vermiglia in ciel*	*C/21
13-14v	Cantata 5ª *Indarno cerca la tortorella*	C/13	181-183v	Cantata Del Vivaldi *Fonti del pianto*	*C/22
15-17v	Cantata Del S. D. Antº. Vivaldi *Elvira, anima mia*	C/14	184-184v	[Blank]	
			185-187v	Cantata Del Vivaldi *Sebben vivono senz'alma*	C/23
18-18v	[Blank]		188-188v	[Blank]	
19-21	Cantata Del S. D. Antº. Vivaldi *Si levi dal pensier*	C/15	189-191v	Cantata Del S. D. Antº. Vivaldi *Sì, sì luci adorate*	C/24
21v-22v	[Blank]		192-192v	[Blank]	
23-24v	Cantata 7ª *Il povero mio cor*	C/16	193-196v	Cantata Del Vivaldi *Era la notte*	C/25
25-25v	[Blank]		197-199	Cantata Del Vivaldi *T'intendo sì mio cor*	C/26
26-29v	Cantata xiiª *Nel partir dà te mio caro*	C/17	199v-200v	[Blank]	
30-32v	Cantata Del S. D. Antº. Vivaldi *Del suo natio rigore*	C/18	201-203	Cantata Del Vivaldi *Alla caccia dell'alme*	*C/27
			203v-204v	[Blank]	
33-36v	Cantata 7ª *All'ombra d'un bel faggio*	C/19	205-208	Cantata Del Vivaldi *Care selve amici prati*	*C/28
37-40v	Cantata Del S. D. Antº. Vivaldi *Aure voi più non siete*	C/20	208v	[Blank]	
			209-302	[Oratorio]	

itative. Vivaldi chooses the *recitativo secco* almost to the exclusion of the *accompagnato* model (the only cantatas in this edition with *recitativo accompagnato* are C/10 and C/12).

Lines of varying length are a disruptive quality in all of Vivaldi's recitatives and are used to create a dramatic quality. Such segments of text and music are separated by various means, according to eighteenth-century convention. For example, the composer may propel the word patterns by using notes of short duration and by fragmenting poetic lines with rests. Cadential formulas set off the larger textual groupings, with the finality of the various stopping points determined by the type of cadence chosen.

Every Vivaldi cantata contains two arias written in *da capo* form. Some of these arias have relatively little vocal display, while others demand a virtuosic technique for their performance. Notated *passaggi* abound in a number of cantatas. Throughout these works, ornamented settings of single words are both decorative and expressive.

The only text that Vivaldi set more than once among the extant cantatas is *Amor hai vinto* (C/3 and C/10). The soprano setting (C/3) has continuo accompaniment while the one for alto (C/10) adds

TABLE 3
Vivaldi Cantatas in Mus. 1/J/7 (Dresden)

Page	Title	Number	Page	Title	Number
58-64	Cantata/Del S. D. Ant°. Vivaldi *Scherza di fronda in fronda*	C/29	96-100	[Title page missing] *Par che tardo*	*C/1
65-72	Cantata/Del Sig^r. D. Ant°. Vivaldi *Geme l'onda che parte*	*C/2	101-112	Cantata/ a Canto Solo con Flauto Tran^v./Del Vivaldi *All'ombra di sospetto*	*C/30
73-80	Cantata Del Vivaldi *Era la notte*	C/25	113-119	Cantata Del Vivaldi *Perfidissimo cor!*	*C/31
81-88	Cantata Del Vivaldi *Fonti del pianto*	*C/22	120	[Blank]	
89-95	Cantata Del Vivaldi *Sorge vermiglia in ciel*	*C/21	121-128	Cantata Del Vivaldi *Pianti, sospiri*	*C/32
			129-136	Cantata Del Vivaldi *Qual per ignoto calle*	*C/33

three stringed instruments. These two works share an intensity and dramatic quality that befits the emotional text.

The Edition

Part I of this edition includes three (C/8, C/11, and C/30) of the four extant cantatas for soprano, continuo, and obbligato instruments; the fourth (C/7) is of lesser musical quality and therefore is not included here. Also included in Part I are five (C/1, C/2, C/3, C/21, and C/22) of the twenty-one extant cantatas for soprano and continuo alone.

Part II contains the five extant cantatas for alto and continuo (C/27, C/28, C/31, C/32, and C/33) and two other alto cantatas (C/10 and C/12) that have obbligato instruments added to the continuo accompaniment. The only other extant alto cantata (C/9) is omitted because it is not of the same quality as the other seven.

The voice range is indicated by the movable clef in all of Vivaldi's cantatas. In the sources, those cantatas for high voice are identified by a soprano clef, while those for a lower range are indicated by an alto clef. This edition uses the G-clef throughout for the vocal part. In both volumes of cantatas, the compositions are grouped according to the type of accompaniment, and are placed alphabetically by the first line of text within that grouping.

The beaming of notes for the vocal line follows Vivaldi's practice, which indicates the syllabifica-

tion and underlaying of the text. Although Vivaldi and his copyists did not always align the text exactly under the appropriate note, the determination of text underlay for this edition was made quite simple by following the beaming of the notes and the proper syllabification of the Italian text.

In some instances, such as *Sorge vermiglia in ciel* where the vocal range is particularly extended, Vivaldi gives a second version of the vocal line by using only note heads (see Plate I, mm. 8, 14-15). The only other examples of this practice in the cantatas of this edition also occur in *Sorge vermiglia in ciel* (Largo, m. 15, where the first two beats are an octave higher; m. 31, where the last half-beat is e″, eighth-note; and m. 32, where the first half-beat is d″, eighth-note).

The tempo designations in the edition are those of the manuscripts. In one instance—the alto *Amor hai vinto* (C/10)—the first aria carries two designations, *Larghetto* and *Andante*. However, the second copy of this cantata (C/10b) lists only *Larghetto*, and this is the choice of tempo in the edition.

The realization of the continuo line appears in cue-size notes. The lowest pitch in the bass clef is that indicated by Vivaldi as the continuo part. This edition reflects only those figures provided in the source. Ms. Mary Mageau realized six of the cantatas (C/1, C/3, C/11, C/21, C/22, and C/30) for performances in 1969. The other cantatas in this edition have been realized by the editor.

Square brackets indicate editorial additions.

Where ornaments or dynamic markings are associated with a motto or subsidiary phrase, Vivaldi does not always write them out again with the reappearances of this material. In such instances, the editor has supplied the appropriate symbols in brackets. When Vivaldi repeats an element of the text, he uses the symbol ∿ rather than fully writing out the text. Where this shorthand occurs, the editor has supplied the text in brackets. Brackets also surround accidentals which are editorially added to correct obvious omissions in the following situations: (1) when one of the instrumental parts or the continuo line has an inflected note and the same pitch is uninflected in the vocal line (or vice versa); (2) when the final note of a measure is inflected and the same pitch is repeated uninflected immediately in the following measure; (3) or when the harmonic movement demands an inflection on one or more pitches. Sometimes the harmonic movement indicates omission of a natural sign, and these necessary naturals are added in brackets. Unnecessary accidentals have been suppressed. Parentheses enclose editorially added cautionary accidentals.

Partial measures occur in the manuscripts when a half-measure completes one system and a full measure is used at the beginning of the new system. In these instances, Vivaldi evidently was using the available space at the end of a staff and failed to complete the measure when he began the next line. In this edition, the meter signature resulting from this practice appears in brackets. Moreover, there are also times when a final measure of a section is not rhythmically complete; the editor has provided the meter signature in brackets in these cases.

The two facsimiles appearing in this edition are from the Foà and Dresden manuscripts, respectively. Plate I (Foà 28) shows Vivaldi's musical and textual writing; in Plate II (Dresden: Mus. 1/J/7) we see Vivaldi's writing of text and the musical notation of a copyist.

The Foà manuscript is the source for this edition when a given cantata (i.e., C/1, C/2, C/21, and C/22) appears in both the Dresden and Foà sources. Variants for these four cantatas are given in the Critical Notes. Part of one cantata (C/1) is omitted in Dresden, and the coloratura passages in the Dresden source are written to avoid b''' and c'''.

The cantata texts appear in the Texts and Translations section in the order in which the works appear in the edition. Since two cantatas (*Amor hai vinto*, C/3 and C/10) share basically the same text, this text is presented only once. Although the translations are literal, they are not meant as a substitution for the Italian text.

Elements of the text, such as single words and certain phrases, are frequently repeated for musical reasons. When the repetition is immediate, the text is set off by a comma and the first word is not capitalized. However, there are numerous instances where a musical cadence occurs before the textual repetition. In this context, a period is used and the first word of the repeated text is capitalized.

The orthography is as it appears in the manuscripts, unless modernization of spelling or the addition of accents was deemed necessary. Such changes are made without editorial comment.

Performance

In addition to written-out ornamentation, Vivaldi also employs conventional symbols. The abbreviation *"tr"* found above quarter- or eighth-notes within a phrase or at a cadence may be generally interpreted as indicating a trill. The composer follows eighteenth-century practice when he frequently writes smaller notes to indicate appoggiaturas.

In the alto *Amor hai vinto* (C/10), Vivaldi uses a short straight line or, in some instances, a marking that looks like an apostrophe to indicate a special effect for the first and second violins (Aria 1, mm. 9-10 and Aria 2, m. 65). These markings do not appear in the performance parts of C/10a. The straight line or apostrophe is probably to be interpreted as a more pronounced staccato than that indicated by a dot.

Several cantatas in the edition have instrumental parts added to the solo voice and continuo part. Vivaldi specifies a solo violin for the arias in *Lungi dal vago volto* (C/8) and a transverse flute for the arias of *All'ombra di sospetto* (C/30). Although the title for the score version of the alto *Amor hai vinto* (C/10) indicates only *con istromenti*, the set of performing parts for this cantata (C/10a) is labeled *Viol° Pr^{mo}, S^{do}*, and *Alto*. *Cessate, omai cessate* (C/12) and *Vengo à voi luci adorate* (C/11) also bear the inscription *con istromenti* in their titles. Since the same number of parts and clefs are involved in C/11 and C/12 as for C/10, the same instrumentation of first and second violin and viola, in addition to the continuo instruments (harpsichord and stringed bass instrument), should probably be employed for these compositions.

Some performance directives appear in the manuscript for *Cessate, omai cessate* (C/12) that indicate orchestral proportions. For example, in the first aria, the two violin parts are to play in unison (*unis^{ni}*) while the directive *"tutti pizziccati; uno con l'arco"* appears above these instrumental lines. The implication is that one violinist plays with the bow while several others play pizzicato. Meanwhile, at this same point, the directive below the continuo part in the manuscript states *"Viol^lo: con arco"* and *"Violone: pizziccato."* That two stringed instruments would be doubling the bass line is unlikely unless several players were also performing each of the other string parts.

We do not know where, when, or by whom Vivaldi's cantatas were performed. However, that Antonio Vivaldi was employed by the Seminario Musicale dell'Ospedale della Pietà from 1703 until 1740 is certain.[10] The Seminario remained one of the tourist attractions listed in the guide books for foreigners throughout the *Settecento,* and concerts in connection with the Sunday liturgy were favorite diversions for travelers as well as for the Venetian nobility.

When the girls of the Seminario gave concerts in the homes of the nobility, they were allowed to mingle with their hosts, under the supervision of their chaperone, the *Priora.* References in the Pietà documents indicate that the girls also were permitted to partake of the festivities and music performances held at the country villas of the Venetian nobility.[11] Perhaps such chamber concerts afforded opportunities for the performance of Vivaldi's cantatas.

The proximity of the rich and worldly convent of San Zaccharia suggests that Vivaldi's students might also have performed his cantatas for the cultured women who lived there. In order to preserve the family patrimony, daughters of the patrician class were often sent to the convent to become nuns.[12] Elegant conversations, balls, theatricals, puppet shows, and concerts were not foreign elements in these convent parlors.

Finally, some of these cantatas are prefaced with a directive that tells how the range may be changed in order to make these works performable by solo singers with varying ranges. The most complete direction for transposing a composition, two flats and the phrase *"Alla 4ª alta"* (at the fourth above), appears in Vivaldi's hand under the title *Cantata* of *Si levi dal pensier* (C/15). Another directive, *"alla 3ª A."* (at the third above), appears on the first page of *All'ombra d'un bel faggio* (C/19); if this is taken literally, the soprano range is altered from f'-a" to a'-c'". Perhaps this cantata was intended for a particular soprano with a well-developed high register.

The directive appearing in the left-hand margin preceding the continuo part of *Il povero mio cor* (C/16) is more difficult to understand. The copyist seems to have written *"4ª: alla 3ª alta"* (fourth [quartet]: at the third above). This directive may indicate that cantatas other than those with instru-

mental parts in the Foà and Dresden manuscripts used an expanded force for the accompaniment when the necessary string players and their parts were available.

Both in detail and larger perspective, the musical settings of these cantatas are fitting for the emotional experience described in the texts. Movements as vivid as these deserve to be heard in contemporary performance.

Critical Notes

When a given cantata exists in both the Turin (Foà 27 and 28) and the Dresden (Mus. 1/J/7) manuscripts, the Foà volumes have been used as the source for the present edition. The first section of Critical Notes lists discrepancies between the Foà source and the Dresden variant for those cantatas contained in both manuscripts. The second section of Critical Notes lists discrepancies between the Foà source or the Dresden source and the present edition. The measure numbers refer to the present edition.

Fonti del pianto

Aria I: M. 18, voice, the second sharp is placed before a'. M. 19, voice, the natural sign appears before d". M. 20, voice, the natural sign is placed before the final note. M. 48, bass, rhythm of notes 1-4 is four sixteenth-notes.

Recitative I: M. 4, bass, D-sharp is given an octave lower.

Aria II: M. 48, bass, final note is g. M. 53, *quanto* is the text (not *guarda* as in Foà); m. 54 gives the text as ◌◌ ; and the first two beats of m. 55 also indicate the text is *quanto* through another ◌◌. M. 65, bass, the final note is e. M. 94, voice, final note is b'. M. 110, voice, the text is underlaid as ♪ ♪ ♫ .
-o mar-to-

Geme l'onda che parte dal fonte

Aria I: M. 9, voice, beat 1 is four sixteenths (a", g", f", e"). M. 13, bass, the second and fourth notes of the final beat are a. Mm. 36-8, bass, from the third beat of m. 36 through the second beat of m. 38, the rhythmic pattern is four sixteenth-notes. M. 33, the bass line is e, eighth notes. Mm. 41-2, voice, the last three notes in m. 41 are c", e", f", and the first two notes in m. 42 are g" and g'. M. 44, voice, last beat consists of four sixteenths (g", a", g", f"). M. 45, voice, first beat consists of four sixteenths (e", d", e", f"). M. 55, voice, notes 4-9 are f", e", f", a", g", f". M. 68, voice, note 2 has *"tr"* symbol above it.

Recitative I: M. 5, voice, third beat contains only b'-flat, quarter-note.

Aria II: M. 8, voice, the first five pitches are g″, e″, d″, c″, g″. M. 9, voice, notes 8-13 are g″, f″, e″, e″, d″, c″. M. 10, voice, notes 4-9 are f″, e″, d″, d″, c″, b′. M. 11, bass, notes 3 and 4 are G, G. M. 15, voice, second half of beat is g″, f″, e″, and beat 3 consists of four sixteenth-notes (d″, g″, f″, g″). M. 23, voice, notes 7-12 are g′, a′, g′, b′, c″, b′. M. 29, voice, last four notes are c″, g″, f″, and e″. M. 30 voice, note 5 is b′. M. 31, voice, last 3 notes are f″, e″, d″. M. 32, voice, first two notes are g″, c″ (eighth-notes). M. 33, bass line is c, eighth-notes. Mm. 49-51, voice, the rhythmic pattern in each measure is four eighth-notes, followed by two groups of four sixteenth-notes. M. 49, voice, the first 5 pitches are d′-sharp, f′-sharp, b′, d″-sharp, d″-sharp, with the latter two pitches tied. M. 50, voice, notes 2-5 are e′, g′, b′, e″. M. 51, voice, notes 3-8 are c″, e″, a″, e″, c″, a′.

Par che tardo

Aria I: Mm. 1-24 are missing. Mm. 28-9, omitted. M. 30 is as follows:

M. 33, bass, sixteenth-rest replaces the first sixteenth-note. M. 35, bass, four final notes are c, c, e, c. Mm. 40-5 in this edition are replaced in Dresden as follows (mm. 40-4):

M. 49, bass, beats 1 and 2 consist of eight sixteenths (a, d, d, d, b, g, g, g). M. 52, bass, beat 3 is an ascending octave leap in eighth-notes. M. 54, bass, beats 1 and 2 consist of eight sixteenths (g, G, G, G, G, G, B, c). M. 56, voice, beat 2, the rhythmic pattern and pitch pattern of m. 55, beat 4 is used, starting on the g″.

Aria II: Mm. 21-3, bass, each of these measures contains the sequential pattern begun in m. 20; the starting pitches are g, a, b-natural. Mm. 36-7 are as follows:

Mm. 42, bass, pitches are A, B-natural, c-sharp, A. M. 43, omitted. M. 44, bass, pitches are d, e, f, d. M. 45, bass, pitches are A, B-natural, c′-sharp, A. M. 52, bass line in this measure is a descending F-scale. Mm. 53-9, omitted. M. 60, bass, note 1 is F. M. 65, voice, last beat is two eighths, f″ and d″; bass, beat 2 is eighth-rest, eighth-note (d). Mm. 66-9, omitted. M. 70, bass, notes 1-4 are all e. M. 76, bass, m. contains four eighths (all e). Mm. 77-8, bass, each m. contains four eighths (all c). Mm. 81-5 of this edition are as follows in Dresden (mm. 81-4):

In Dresden, the pitches of m. 80 (this edition) are the same, but Vivaldi starts the word *riposo* on the last pitch. Because the Dresden version has one less measure for this phrase, he does not repeat *riposo*, and goes immediately to *avrò*. In Dresden, therefore, the text is *riposo avrò*, whereas in this edition, it is *ristoro, ristoro avrò*. Mm. 105-20 of this edition appear in the following contracted version in Dresden:

Sorge vermiglia in ciel

Recitative I: M. 3, voice, beat 3 is two eighth-notes (both d′-sharp), first half of beat 4 is eighth-note c″. M. 4, voice, appoggiatura on note 5 omitted. M. 8, voice, notes 2-5 are d″. M. 10, voice, notes 5 and 6 are g″. M. 13, voice, last 5 notes are d″, b′-flat, a″-flat, g″, f″. M. 14, voice, last 2 notes are a′, g′. M. 15, voice, notes 1 and 2 are both e′-flat.

Aria I: M. 7, bass, last 2 notes are sharped. M. 10, voice, last note is g″. M. 11, voice, notes 1-4 are g″, a′, a′, e″; bass, notes 3-6 are c-sharp, B-natural, c-sharp, A. M. 13, voice, last 4 notes are c″, b′, g′, d″; bass notes are A, B-natural, c-sharp, B-natural, A, a, e, c-sharp. M. 14, voice, note 1 is d''. M. 15, voice, text underlay omits the words *Sempre lungi*; vocal pitches are f'-sharp, d'', e'', d'', c''-sharp, d'' (eighth, 2 sixteenths, 2 eighths, quarter), and final beat is quarter-rest; bass line pitches are d, f, g, a, d, d, e, c. M. 18, voice, all trill symbols omitted. M. 19, bass, notes 1-5 are f, f, g, g, a. M. 22, voice, notes 5-7 are e''-flat, g'', g''. Mm. 23-31 of this edition appear as follows in Dresden (mm. 23-32):

Mm. 35-6, voice, first 6 pitches are an octave higher. Mm. 43-6, the ending of Aria I is as follows:

Recitative II: M. 7, bass, m. contains half-note (d) and 2 quarters (e and A). M. 8, bass, m. contains whole-note (A). M. 12, voice, notes 1 and 2 are both a'. M. 13, b-natural indicated in signature.

Aria II: M. 1, bass, g and f are sharped. Mm. 14-15, voice part is a third higher. M. 21, bass, beat 4 contains 2 eighth-notes (c and c'). M. 24, bass, beat 2 contains 2 eighth-notes (A and a); voice, beats 3 and 4 are 4 eighth-notes (a'', f'', d'', a'). M. 36, bass, beat 4 is 2 eighths (A, B). M. 46, voice, note 6 is e'. M. 49, bass, beats 3 and 4 are four eighths (A, a, a,

a). M. 60, bass, beats 3 and 4 are four eighth-notes (e, a, d-sharp, B). M. 61, bass, notes 6 and 7 are a and d-sharp. Mm. 62-6 are omitted.

Discrepancies between the present edition and the Foà source or Dresden source are listed below.

Lungi dal vago volto

Aria II: M. 114, vn. part is omitted.

Vengo à voi luci adorate

Aria I: M. 46, vla., notes 5-8 are all e'.
Aria II: M. 15, voice and vn. I, note 1 of beat 4 is d''.

Pianti, sospiri

Recitative I: M. 1, bass, note 2 is e. M. 48, bass, note 4 is A-sharp.

Qual per ignoto calle

Recitative II: M. 6, voice, note 5 is d'-flat.
Aria II: M. 5, bass, penultimate note is F. M. 70, bass note 1 is f.

Amor hai vinto (C/10)

Aria I: M. 29, vn. II, note 1 is e''.
Recitative I: M. 20, voice, note 3 is a sixteenth.
Aria II: M. 72, vn. II, final 4 notes are f''-sharp, g'', a'', g''.

Cessate, omai cessate

Aria I: M. 29, only 3 is indicated as a meter signature at this point.

Acknowledgments

Direct work with the manuscripts was made possible by grants from the Rackham Dissertation Fund, the University of Michigan (1968), and the National Endowment for the Humanities (1970). Microfilm was provided by the Biblioteca Nazionale di Torino and the Sächsische Landesbibliothek (Dresden), for which I am most appreciative. I am grateful to Professor Vincent Scanio of the University of Michigan for his help in deciphering the handwritten texts and translating the poetry.

Meneve Dunham
Clarke College
Dubuque, Iowa

April 1979

Notes

1. These major studies are: Remo Giazotto, *Vivaldi* (Milan, 1965); Walter Kolneder, *Antonio Vivaldi, Leben und Werke* (Wiesbaden, 1965); Marc Pincherle, *Antonio Vivaldi et la musique instrumentale* (Paris, 1948); and Mario Rinaldi, *Antonio Vivaldi* (Milan, 1943).

2. Antonio Vivaldi, *Opere,* ed. Istituto Italiano Antonio Vivaldi fondata Antonio Fanna e artistica direzione Gian Francesco Malipiero (Edizioni Ricordi, 1947-   ).

3. In the Tables on pp. viii-x, the editor has assigned numbers to the cantatas contained in the Foà and Dresden sources.

4. See Meneve Dunham, "The Secular Cantatas of Antonio Vivaldi in the Foà Collection" (Ph.D. diss., University of Michigan, 1969), pp. 36-8, for a description of these two volumes.

5. The Foà cantatas which are duplicated in Mus. 1/J/7 (Eitner Lexicon, B835) are C/1, C/2, C/21, C/22, and C/25. Table 3 lists only the Vivaldi cantatas in this Dresden manuscript.

6. In this Florentine anthology, the cantatas numbered 11 *(Piango, gemo, sospiro)*, 13 *(Ingrate Lidia)*, and 14 *(Filli, di goia farmi morir)* are ascribed to Vivaldi (Biblioteca del Conservatorio, D-II-569).

7. Giazotto, *Vivaldi,* p. 189.

8. See Dunham, "Secular Cantatas," p. 64, for the text and setting of the three incomplete recitatives.

9. In reference to the sonnets published with Vivaldi's *Concerti delle Stagioni* (Op. 8, 1-4), Giazotto states that he believes Vivaldi wrote his own texts because of the close relationship between textual idea and musical means. See Giazotto, *Vivaldi,* p. 156.

10. For a chronology of Vivaldi's life, see Dunham, "Secular Cantatas," pp. 4-10.

11. The records of the Pietà are held in the Venetian State Archives under the title *Ospedali e Luoghi Pii diversi,* 265-II-209. For the period 1762-97, expense books (Bu. 694) list the monies given to the girls for trips to the villas.

12. Pompeo Molmenti, *Storia di Venezia nella vita privata* (Venezia, 1910), 2:82.

Texts and Translations

Amor hai vinto

Recitative

Amor hai vinto.
Ecco il mio seno
da tuo bel stral traffitto
or chi sostiene
l'alma mia dal dolore abbandonata!
Gelido in ogni vena
scorrermi sento il sangue,
e sol mi serba(n) in vita
affanni, e pene.
Mi palpita nel seno
con nuove scosse il core.
Clori crudel,
e quanto hà dà durar
quest'aspro tuo rigore?

(Love, you have conquered. Here is my breast wounded by your beautiful arrow; now who sustains my abandoned soul from grief! I feel my blood, icy-cold in my veins, flow; only uneasiness and pain preserve me in life. My heart throbs in my breast with new blows. Cruel Chloris, how long is your harsh severity to continue?)

Aria

Passo di pena in pena
Come la navicella ch'in questa
E in quell'altr'onda
Urtando và.
Il ciel tuona e balena
Il mar tutt'è in tempesta
Porto non vede, ò sponda
Dove approdar non sà.

(I pass from pain to pain as a ship, which goes knocking against first one wave and then another. The sky thunders and lightnings; the sea is all in a tempest. The ship sees no port or bank; it knows not where to land.)

Recitative

In qual strano, e confuso
vortice di pensieri
la mia mente s'aggira?
Or'è in calma, or s'adira,
e dove ancor si fermi, non risolve.
Or in sasso, o in polve,
vorria cangiarsi.

Oh Dio! Mà di che mai,
mà di che ti querelli
cor incredulo infido?
Di che ti lagni, ahime!
forse non sai
che nel seno di Clori
hai porto, hai lido!

(In what strange and confused swirl of thoughts is my mind tossed? Now it is in a state of calm, now a state of anger and can not resolve itself. First it will wish to change itself into stone, now into dust. Oh God! But what in the world, what are you querulous about, you unbelieving, faithless heart? Of what do you complain, alas! Perhaps you know not that in the breast of Chloris you have a port, a shore!)

Aria

Se à me rivolge il ciglio
L'amato mio tesoro
Non sento più martoro
Mà torno à respirar.
Non teme più periglio
Non sente affanno, e pena
L'alma, e si rasserena
Come la calma in mar.

(If my loved treasure turns her eyes to me, I no longer feel torment, but return to live. The soul no longer fears danger, no longer feels trouble; it becomes serene again as the calm on the sea.)

Fonti del pianto

Aria

Fonti del pianto
Piangete tanto
Sino che in lagrime
Struggasi il cor.
Mio cor amante
Sei di diamante
S'oggi non spezzati
Al mio dolor.

(Weep so much, oh fountains of tears, until the heart melts in tears. My loving heart, you are made of diamond if today she does not break you because of my sorrow.)

Come cor più spietato
non v'è del duro cor
della mia Filli,
così più desolato
nò che non v'è di te,
mio cor amante.
Al fido, ella incostante,
tu l'ami, ella t'abborre,
tu la segui, ella ti fugge.
À duol cotanto,
se resister non puoi
struggiti afflito cor
struggiti in pianto.

(As there is not a more pitiless heart than the hard heart of my Phyllis, so there is not a more desolate one than you, my loving heart. To your faith, she is inconstant; you love her, she abhors you; you follow her, she runs from you. If you are not able to resist so much sorrow, destroy yourself afflicted heart, melt into tears.)

Aria

Guarda nè gl'occhi miei
Filli spietata oh Dio!
Quanto crudel tu sei
Quanto fedel son io
Quanto t'adoro.
E come è in me l'amore
Equal à tua bellezza
Rimira entro il mio core,
Equal à tua fierezza
Il mio martoro.

(Look into my eyes. Oh God, pitiless Phyllis, how cruel you are; how faithful am I, to what extent I adore you. And just as in me, love is equal to your beauty; gaze into my heart, my torment is equal to your harshness.)

Geme l'onda che parte dal fonte

Aria

Geme l'onda che parte dal fonte,
Langue il fiore, che il sole non vede,
E in la valle, nel prato e su'l monte
Sempre in pianto ora parte ora riede
Usignuol che l'amante perde.
Mà non geme non langue nè piange
Quell' augello quel fior e quell'onda
Come il cor che nel petto si frange
Come l'alma, cui duolo circonda,
Caro Tirsi, lontana dà te.

(The wave which leaves the fountain laments, the flower which does not see the sun languishes, and in the valley, in the meadow, and on the mountain, the ever-tearful nightingale, who lost his loved one, now leaves, now returns. But that bird, flower, and wave do not weep, languish, nor lament as does the broken heart, as does the soul surrounded by sorrow, far from you, dear Tirsi.)

Recitative

Ah ch'un immensa doglia
tutta mi strugge in pianto,
è non sò come questa,
ch'in te sol vive
alma d'amor ferita
Lunghe dà gl'occhi tuoi rimanga in vita.
Sò ben che se la speme di ritornar
à vagheggiarti ancora
non tempra neun dolor così inhumano,
ciò che non fece il duol fara la mano.
Che men fiero sarebbe, e rio martire,
una volta morir, che ogn'or languire.

(Ah, an immense pain melts me into tears; how is it that this soul wounded by love and which lives in you alone, yet far from your eyes, still remains alive. I know very well that if the hope of returning once again to gaze fondly upon you will not appease a grief so inhuman, that which sorrow will not do, the hand will. For less harsh and terrible pain would it be to die once than to languish forever.)

Aria

Deh non partir si presto
Conforto del mio cor
Ristoro al mio penar
Cara speranza.
Serbami al mio diletto
In onta à quel dolor
Che tenta d'atterrar
La mia costanza.

(Pray, do not leave so quickly, comfort of my heart, refreshment to my suffering, dear hope. Preserve me for my delight in spite of that sorrow which is attempting to fell my constancy.)

Par che tardo

Aria

Par che tardo oltre il costume
Oggi scenda al mar d'Atlante
Il bel Dio che col suo lume
E la terra, e il ciel rischiara.

Ed intanto il core amante,
Cui l'occaso appresta un bene
Trova il duol nella sua spene
E à soffrir godendo impara.

(It seems that late beyond its customary way, the
lovely god, which with his light brightens the land
and sky, descends to the sea of Atlante. And meanwhile the loving heart, for whom the sunset is preparing a good thing, finds sorrow in his hope and
learns to suffer while enjoying.)

RECITATIVE

Quando tu d'Anfitrite
in grembo giacerai,
celeste Auriga,
io della bella Clori
in grembo goderò felice amante.
Di tante pene e tante
per lei sofferte
avrò dolce ristoro
de' miei sospir,
del duol del lungo pianto.
Deh à dar pace al mio core
affretta, o sol,
affretta il corso alquanto.

(When you will lie on the bosom of Amphitrite,
heavenly charioteer, I, on the bosom of the beautiful Chloris, will enjoy myself as a happy lover. Forever so many pains and sufferings because of her, I
shall have sweet rest from the sighs of the pain of
long weeping. O, to give peace to my heart, hasten
oh sun, hasten your course somewhat.)

ARIA

All'or che in cielo
Notte il suo velo distenderà.
In braccio à Clori
De' miei dolori, ristoro avrò.
De' scorsi affanni
Amor i danni compenserà
E la mia fede
Dolce mercede ritroverò.

(At that time in the sky, the night will extend her
veil; in the arms of Chloris, I shall find refreshment
from my sorrows. For past troubles, love and my
faith will compensate for the damages, and I will
find sweet reward.)

Sorge vermiglia in ciel

RECITATIVE

Sorge vermiglia in ciel la bella Aurora,
ed io dolente allora per crudeltà

d'amor di pena in pena mi vò struggendo,
oh Dio, senza sperar pietà del dolor mio.
Quando tra l'ombre poi Espero luce
raddoppiarmi all'or sento
il mio fiero tormento;
E così passo sempre i giorni, e l'ore,
e quando nasce il sol, e quando muore.

(A beautiful dawn rises pink in the sky, and I, griev-
ing then because of the cruelty of love, go about
from pain to pain, dying, oh God, without hope of
pity for my sorrow. When midst the shadows then
the evening star shines, doubly I feel my fiery torment. And thus I pass always the days and hours,
when the day breaks and when the sun sets.)

ARIA

Nasce il sole
Ed io sospiro perche miro,
Che l'ingrata Pastorella
Sempre lungi dà me và.
Muore il sole,
E allor io sento un tormento
Che nel seno il cor vien meno,
Se non hà di me pietà.

(Day breaks and I sigh because I see that the ungrateful shepherdess always goes far away from
me. The sun sets and then I feel a torment, for in
my breast my heart faints away if she does not have
pity on me.)

RECITATIVE

Ah, Silvia, tu sei quella crudele Pastorella,
che sazia ancor non sei di tormentarmi.
Se à pascere l'armento io ti ritrovo
il mio diletto egl'è di rimirarti;
Mà quando alla capanna fai ritorno
perdo tutto il piacer di vagheggiarti.
Se ti seguo, mi fuggi,
se ti parlo d'amor, fiera, e spietata,
mi schernisci, e m'offendi,
e la pace al mio cor vieti, e contendi.
Mà se sapessi almeno,
come placare un dì la tua fierezza!
Oh Dio! che posso sol nel mio martire,
amarti col sperare, e col soffrire.

(Ah Silvia! You are that cruel shepherdess who is
not yet satisfied with tormenting me. If I find you
feeding the flock, my delight is to gaze upon you;
but when you return to the hut, I lose all my pleas-
ure of cherishing you. If I follow you, you flee me;
if I speak to you of love, you, fierce and pitiless,
sneer at me and offend me and forbid peace to my
heart; and you contend. But if you could know one

day at least how to placate your boldness! Oh God! I am only able with hope and suffering to love you in my martyrdom.)

ARIA

Ardi, svena, impiaga, atterra
Sino il ciel, i Dei, la terra
Sveglia pur contro di me.
Con martir, pena, e dolore l'odio,
L'ira, e'l tuo rigore sazia pure,
Mà costante sarà sempre la mia fè.

(Burn, bleed, wound, beat to the ground the gods from the heavens; awake even the earth against me. With tribulations, pains, and sorrowing satiate then hatred, anger, and even your harshness; but my faith will always be constant.)

All'ombra di sospetto

RECITATIVE

All'ombra di sospetto
il mio costante, affetto
perde alquanto la fede,
e à beltà lusingie va
ei poco crede.

(From the shadow of suspicion, my constancy, suffering, loses somewhat its confidence, and to such beautiful allurement, some trust departs.)

ARIA

Avezzo non è il core,
Amar beltà d'amore
Ch'addolcisca il penar
Con finti vezzi.
Se lusingiero è il dardo
Ogni piacer è tardo
À fia che l'adorar
Per forza sprezzi.

(The heart is not accustomed to the bitter-sweetness of love, which soothes suffering with its feigned charm. Scorn will come to those who love passionately on impulse.)

RECITATIVE

Ò quanti amanti, ò quanti
che fedeli e costanti regon delusi
dà lusinghe accorte
d'amor frà le ritorte.
Più d'ogni un così langue,
e tante volte il sangue
spargeria per mostrar

il vero amore.
Concetto dall'ardore
di vezzosa bellezza
ch'ogn'or gli strugge l'alma
ed al suo affetto calma
mai spera di goder,
sin ch'ingannato
viene amante schernito,
e ingannato.

(O, how many lovers, true and faithful, are deluded by shrewd flattery amid the chains of love. Many languish, and frequently blood is shed to prove true love. Formed from the ardor of charming beauty, the soul struggles each hour, and the derided lover is deceived again and again.)

ARIA

Mentiti contenti
Son veri tormenti
D'amante fedel.
Gran male è qual bene
Son dardi quei guardi,
Che vibran per pene
Bellezza crudel.

(False happiness is the real torture of the loving follower. Merciless beauty has darts, those glances that waver with distress.)

Lungi dal vago volto

RECITATIVE

Lungi dal vago volto
della mia bella Elvira
viver non posso.
Oh Dio! e pur crudo
destin per mio tormento
or mi condanna à pascolar l'armento,
mà qual da lunghi ammira
non distinta beltade
il guardo mio Pastorella che viene?
Temo d'error, mi perdo
corro, ivi fermo rido,
e sospiro ad un ardo,
gelo contento, e tormentato:
si sembra alla divisa
non mi par al sembiante
deh per pietade amor amico cielo
sciogli dal mio bel sol
la nube il velo.

(I am not able to live far from the charming face of my beautiful Elvira. Oh God! and crude destiny, also, for my torment, now sentences me to pasture the flock; but, of whom, from a distance does my glance admire, the indistinct beauty, the shepherd-ess who comes? I fear that I am seeing things; I lose myself. I run there; I stop, I laugh, and I sigh. I burn; I freeze, happy and tormented: it seems to me by her dress that it is she; but it does not seem so by her face. Pray, out of pity, lovely, friendly sky, re-move from my beautiful sun the cloud, the veil.)

ARIA

Augelletti voi col canto
Queste selve impretiosite.
Ed io posso sol col pianto
Consolare il mio dolor.
Fate voi che dolce incanto
Con amor ò con pietade e
Chiami al bosco il mio tesor.

(Little birds, you with song make precious these woods, and I am able only with tears to comfort my sorrow. Bring about that sweet enchantment with love or with pity; and call to the woods my treasure.)

RECITATIVE

Allegrezza mio core
ch'al fin giunse alla meta
l'avida mia pupilla
ti riconosco ò bella
ti riveggio mio bene
l'abbraccio Pastorella.
Perdona ò cara
à miei sospesi affetti
perche errante Pastor
veder non suole
tra queste ombrose frondi
aperto il sole.

(Be joyful my heart, for at the end my eager eyes succeeded to the goal. I recognize you, oh beauty! I see you again my beloved; I embrace the shepherd-ess. Excuse, o dearest, my suspended affections be-cause the wandering shepherd is not accustomed to sunlight amid these shadowy leaves.)

ARIA

Mi stringerai sì, sì,
Non partirai più nò.
Bella ti rapirò
Se il cor non cede.
Avvinto al tuo bel sen
Ti giuro amato ben
Che mai ti mancherò
D'amor, e fede.

(Yes, you will draw near; no, you will not leave any more. Beautiful one, I will carry you away if your heart does not surrender. Bound to your lovely bosom, I swear to you my loved one that I will never fail you with respect to love and faith.)

Vengo à voi luci adorate

ARIA

Vengo à voi luci adorate
Per dar tregua à tante pene
E ritorno à adorarvi.
Io ritorno luci adorate
Ad adorarvi.
Benche siate tanto ingrate
Care luci del mio bene
Io lasciar non vo' d'amarvi.

(I come to you, beloved eyes, in order to give truce to so many pains; once again I return to adore you. I return, beloved eyes, to adore you. Even though you, dear eyes, are so unconcerned about my wel-fare, I do not wish to stop loving you.)

RECITATIVE

Portando in sen l'ardor,
che m'accendeste un giorno
idolatra fedel à voi ritorno.
Mà se foste pietoso
ristoro voi non date al mio gran foco
datemi almen la morte
perche troppo insoffribile
martire viver nel foco
è non poter morire.

(Carrying in my breast the ardor which one day you, idolator, enkindled, I return faithfully to you. You do not give relief to my great ardor; but, if you were merciful, you would give me death at least. For it is too insufferable to live in the fire as a martyr and not be able to die.)

ARIA

Sempre penare senza speranza
È un gran tormento occhi tiranni.
Ne val sperare dalla costanza
Un sol momento in tanti affani.

(Always to suffer without hope is a great torment, oh tyrannical eyes. Nor does it avail to hope, be-cause of perseverance, for a single moment in so many tribulations.)

Alla caccia dell'alme

ARIA

Alla caccia dell'alme,
E de' cori
La barbara Clori
Amanti sen và.
Già i lacci dispone
Le reti già stende
Al varco v'attende
Quell'empia beltà.

(The barbarous Chloris, oh you lovers, goes away to hunt for souls and hearts. Already she places the snares; already she extends the nets. At the passage, this impious beauty awaits you.)

RECITATIVE

Mà sia crudele ò infida,
oh Dio, mi piace.
E sebben sia spietato
dà quel bel volto, o cor,
tu sei legato.

(But whether she is cruel or faithless, she is pleasing to me. Oh God! And, although you are hurt, oh heart, you are bound by that beautiful face.)

ARIA

Preso sei mio cor piagato
Non sperar più
Dalla bella servitu
Di poter spiegar il volo.
Consolar bensi ti puoi
Ch'à provare i lacci suoi
Non sei primo e non sei solo.

(My wounded heart, you are caught. Do not hope any more to spread your flight from this beautiful bondage. Certainly you are able to console yourself, for in undergoing her snares you are not the first, and you are not alone.)

Care selve amici prati

RECITATIVE

Care selve amici prati
À cercar ritorno in voi
La perduta amabil pace.
Quella pace, che spietati
Mi rapir coi pensier suoi
Speme infida amor fallace.

(Dear woods, friendly meadows, I return to you in search of my lost, beloved peace. This peace, which faithless hope, fallacious love with its thoughts, pitilessly snatched from me.)

RECITATIVE

Ben mal'accorto,
e folle all'or io fui,
che vaghezza mi prese
di migliorar mia sorte,
e per tal sorte
lunge dal natio bosco il piè portai.
Infelice mi rese
una speme si ardita.
Ove sperai grandezze ritrovar,
trovai rovine.
Tu insano d'arricchir cieco desio
tu ingannasti il cor mio,
e pace, e libertà per te perdei.
Or scoperto l'inganno
riedo à viver in quiete i giorni miei,
e à reparar dal tempo corso il danno.

(I was unaware and foolish then, and desire to improve my destiny overtook me. Through such fate, I wandered afar from my native woods. A hope so ardent made me unhappy. Where I hoped to find greatness, I found ruins. You, insane through a blind desire to become rich, you deceived my heart, and I lost peace and liberty through you. Now that deceit has been uncovered, I return to live my days in quiet and to repair the damage of the past.)

ARIA

Placido in letto ombroso
Là dove scorre il rio
Stesso su'l margo ombroso
Dell'onda al mormorio,
Il canto accorderò.
Condur il gregge amato
Sola mia cura fia,
Dalla capana al prato,
E in onta à sorte ria
Contento viverò contento goderò.

(In a peaceful shady bed, there where the stream flows, I, stretched out on the shady bank, will harmonize my song with the murmuring of the wave. My only care will be to lead my loved flock from the hut to the meadow; and in spite of evil destiny, I shall live in contentment and happily enjoy myself.)

Perfidissimo cor!

Perfidissimo cor! Iniquo fato!
Iniquissimo amor! Tirsi spietato.
Dov'è, dov'è l'amore,
che per me' nel tuo core si nutriva?
Ah, lungi dal tuo petto
svani si fermo affetto.
Io sò bene, lo sò,
che se un amante
ottiene ciò che brama
di poi più non si cura.
Ah disleal, ah ingrato!
Perfidissimo cor, Tirsi spietato.

(Most wicked heart! Most treacherous love! Tirsi so ruthless. Where, oh where, is the love with which I nourished your heart? Ah, far from your breast, this strong affection is lost. I know well, oh so well, that this lover gained an ardent desire from which it can no longer cure itself. Ah disloyalty, ah ingratitude! Most wicked heart, Tirsi so ruthless.)

ARIA

Nel torbido mio petto
S'aggira un ombra squallida
Di sdegno, e crudeltà.
E questi la vendetta
Che cancellar pretende
L'onta d'infedeltà.

(In the turbulence of my heart, a dreary shadow roves with disdain and cruelty. And this shadow is the revenge that claims to wipe out the shame of infidelity.)

RECITATIVE

Così dunque tradisci,
chi contenta t'offerse
i primi affetti?
Dimmi qual fede mai
infido aver' tu puoi,
se chiaro vedi,
che di tua fe' il candore
si rassomiglia alla vernale brina,
che tocca un poco dall'artura face
in niente tutta si dissolve,
e sface.
Così per te ò inhumana
per crederti in amor ogn'una cede.
Misera amante è quella, che ti crede.

(Thus, then, do you deceive the one who happily gave you all love? Tell me what trust you, ever unfaithful, have given then. If you see clearly, that with your trust, honesty resembles the hoar frost, which when touched a little by the torch becomes nothing; all is dissolved and darkened. Thus, through you so inhuman and through love believing you, each one yields. The suffering lover is the one who believes you.)

ARIA

Più amar' non spero nò
Se il primo m'inganno
E infido mi tradi.
Misera ancor per me
Che ancor non spero fe'
Se l'amor mio svani.

(Filled with bitterness, I do not hope. At first you deceive me, and unfaithful you betray me. Suffering remains for me; for again I do expect fidelity if love is lost.)

Pianti, sospiri

RECITATIVE

Pianti, sospiri,
e dimandar mercede lusinghe son
di femmina incostante,
che per vantarsi amante
d'un incorotta fede
dar per pegno d'affetto.
Mà che poi nel suo petto
vi regni un tal amor,
ah non è vero;
sei pianti, ed i sospiri,
e la chiesta mercè
d'amante brama
si cangia di repente
in risi, in vezzi,
ed in lasciar, chi l'ama.

(Weeping, sighing, and asking recompense, one is flattered by a fickle woman, who gives a sign of affection while fondly boasting of her undying trust. Then she rules within his breast with a great love. Ah, it is not true; you are tears and sighs. The requested mercy of ardent desire is changed suddenly in laughter, in charms, and in leaving her who delighted in it.)

ARIA

Lusingha è del nocchier
Quel venticel leggier
Che placido lo invitta
À solcar l'onde.

Mà fuor del porto appena
I fiati suoi scatena,
E il scampo alla sua vita
Allor nasconde.

(The helmsman is deceived by the gentle wind that invites him to sail the seas. But hardly out of port, the winds are unleashed, and then the safety of his life is hidden.)

RECITATIVE

O ingannato nocchiero
troppo incanto à dar fede
à mobil aurà.
Ti lasciasti condur fuori del porto,
e appena visto il mar,
restasti absorto.
Mà è più deluso amante,
che nel mare d'amore
d'aura fallace d'amorosa speme
allettato il suo core,
mentre spiegà il desio
del proprio affetto,
e vo improviso oh Dio
di sdegno, e d'odio insieme
un turbine lo assale empio,
e malvaggio,
che predice al suo cor
un rio naufraggio.

(Oh, deceived helmsman, so bewitched as to put trust in the changing winds. You let yourself be guided out of the port, and as soon as the sea is calmed, you are kept from your destination. But the more disappointed lover is the one whose heart is allured in the sea of love by the deceitful breezes of loving hope while the desire of his own affection unfolds and changes suddenly, oh God, both to indignation and hatred. A whirlwind, vile and wicked, assails him, warning his heart of an evil shipwreck.)

ARIA

Cor ingrato dispietato
Sol racchiude inganni e offese
Sol nudrisce infedeltà.
Mà poi vuole giusto il cielo
Che se prova il stral d'amore
Non ritrovi che rigore,
Che disprezzi, e crudeltà.

(A heart displaying ingratitude holds only deceits and offenses, and nourishes only infidelities. But then it rightly wishes the heavens to prove the arrows of love do not return that harshness, contempt, and cruelty.)

Qual per ignoto calle

RECITATIVE

Qual per ignoto calle
muove dubbioso pellegrino
il piede, desio l'incalza,
e reo timor l'arresta;
Nel profondo di tetra orrida valle,
senza raggio di stella
caliginosa notte il preme,
e lo circonda.
Terribile tempesta
di spessi tuoni, e lampi
lo sbigottito cor
preme, e flagella;
Pur vinto del desio prende coraggio,
timor non cuore
e segue il suo viaggio.
Tal misero son io,
che nel sentier d'amore,
benche d'aspro rigore
provi armata colei
che mi vuol morto,
pur con occulta forza non manca,
e non si smorza in me la fiama,
e spero alfin conforto.

(As the hesitant pilgrim moves through the unknown streets, desire presses him, and guilty fear stops him. In the depths of the dismal, terrible valley, without the light of a star, the dark night enfolds and surrounds him. A terrible storm, with frequent thunder and lightning, pursues and torments the discouraged heart. Still overcome by desire, take courage. Fear not heart and continue the journey. Such misery I have, that in the path of love filled with harsh rigors, you show armed that woman who wishes me death. Yet concealed force is not lacking; the flame is not extinguished within me, and hope at last brings comfort.)

ARIA

Quel passegier son io
Che vo cercando in te
Mia bella amore, e fe',
E sol ritrovo, oh Dio
Rigore e crudeltà.
E pur costante Irene
Bella nemica mia
Men orgogliosa, e rio
Spero che di mie pene
Un giorno a rai pietà.

(I am that traveler who goes searching for you, my beautiful love and faith, and I only find harshness and cruelty. And yet unremitting Irene, my beautiful enemy, less haughty and wicked, I hope that from my pain one day I will have mercy.)

RECITATIVE

Deh più non regni
nel tuo gentil petto
una si fiera voglia,
che mal conviensi à delicato viso
di voler la mia morte doppio
tanti tormenti e tante pene.
Cangia dunq; ben amio, cangia consiglio;
Volgi sereno il ciglio à me, che t'amo,
d'un amor si forte, che mai per tempo,
o variar di loco s'estinguerà si caro,
e gentil fuoco.

(Alas! reign no more in your gentle breast a desire so fierce that evil comes to your delicate face by wishing my death, doubling my many torments. Change then; my love, follow my advice. Turn calmly your eyes to me, who loves you with a love so strong, who never, through time or change of place, will extinguish the flame so dear and gentle.)

ARIA

Qual doppo lampi, e turbini
Appar l'Aurora fulgida
À dissipar le tenebre d'oscura notte orribile
E il pellegrino timido ritorna à consolar.
Cosí men fiero, e rigido se volgi à me
L'amabile ciglio ridente, e placido
Pieno d'amor di giubilo scordato di mie lacrime
Benedirò il penar.

(As after the lightning and thunder the radiant dawn appears to dissipate the darkness of the obscure, terrible night, so the timid pilgrim returns to rejoice. Thus, less haughty and austere, you turn to me your loving, bright eyes; and calmly, full of the love of jubilation and forgetting my tears, I will bless my suffering.)

Cessate, omai cessate

RECITATIVE

Cessate, omai cessate,
rimembranze crudeli
d'un affetto tiranno;
Già barbare e spietate
mi cangiaste i contenti
in un immenso affanno.
Cessate, omai cessate,
di lacerarmi il petto,
di trafigermi l'alma,
di toglier al mio cor
riposo, e calma.
Povero core afflitto,
e abbandonato, se ti toglie la pace
un affetto tiranno,
perche un volto spietato,
un alma infida,
la sola crudeltà pasce ed annida.

(Cease, now cease, oh cruel memories of a tyrannical love; in the past you barbarous and pitiless memories changed my joy into an intense suffering. Cease, now cease, to lacerate my bosom, to transfix my soul and to remove from my heart peace and calm. Poor heart, afflicted and abandoned; if a tyrannical love removes peace from you, the reason is a pitiless face. An unfaithful soul feeds and lives only on cruelty.)

ARIA

Ah ch'infelice sempre
Me vuol Dorilla ingrata,
Ah sempre più spietata
M'astringe à lagrimar.
Per me non v'è nò, non v'è ristoro
Per me non v'è nò, non v'è più speme.
E il fier martoro e le mie pene,
Solo la morte può consolar.

(Ah, ungrateful Dorilla always wishes me unhappiness, and even more pitiless, she forces me to cry. For me, no, there isn't any refreshment; for me, no, there is no hope any longer. And only death can console the fiery martyrdom and my pain.)

RECITATIVE

À voi dunque ricorro orridi specchi,
taciturni orrori, solitaris ritiri,
ed ombre amiche trà voi
porto il mio duolo,
perche spero dà voi quella pietade,
che Dorilla inhumana non annida.
Vengo, spelonche amate,
vengo specchi graditi,
affine meco involto
il mio tormento in voi
resti sepolto.

(To you, therefore I return; horrid caves, silent horrors, solitary retreats and friendly shadows. Within you I carry my sorrow because I hope from you that pity which does not nestle in the inhuman Dorilla. I come, loved caverns, grateful caves, in order that my torment wrapped within me may be buried in you.)

xxiv

ARIA

Nell'orrido albergo ricetto di pene
Potrò il mio tormento sfogare contento
Potrò ad alta voce chiamare spietata
Dorilla l'ingrata, morire potrò.
Andrò d'Acheronte sù le nera sponda,
Tingendo quest'onda di sangue innocente
Gridando vendetta,

Ed ombra baccante vendetta farò.

(In this horrid shelter, a refuge from pain, I shall happily be able to give vent to my torment; I shall be able to call in a loud voice upon ungrateful, pitiless Dorilla; I shall be able to die. I will go to the black bank of Acheron, dyeing this wave with innocent blood, crying revenge, and as a furious shade, I shall have vengeance.)

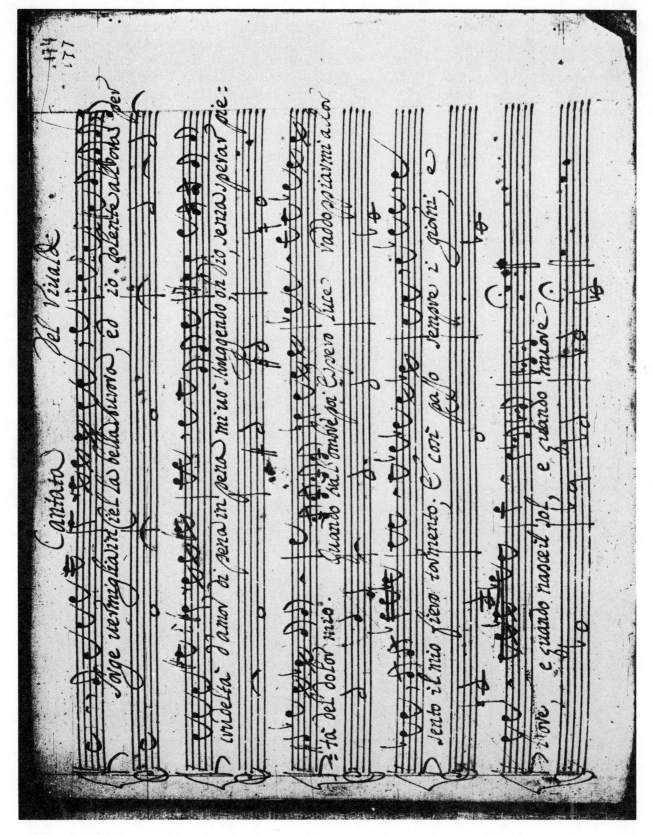

Plate I. *Sorge vermiglia in ciel* (C/21), first recitative.
(Courtesy, Biblioteca Nazionale di Torino)

Plate II. *Fonti del pianto* (C/22), first aria.
(Courtesy, Sächsische Landesbibliothek, Dresden)

CANTATAS FOR SOLO VOICE
Part I: Soprano

Amor hai vinto

A- mor hai vin- to, hai vin- to. Ec - co il mio

se- no da tuo bel stral traf- fit- to or chi so-

-stie- ne l'al- ma mia dal do- lo- re ab-ban-do- na- ta!

Ge- li- do in o- gni ve- na scor- rer- mi sen- to il san- gue, e

sol mi ser- ba in vi- ta af- fan- ni, e pe- ne. Mi

pal- pi- ta nel se- no con nuo- ve scos- se il co- re.

Clo- ri cru- del, e quan- to hà dà du- rar que- st'a- spro tuo ri- go- re?

Largo

Pas- so di pe- na in pe - na, di

pe- na in pe- na   Co- me la na- vi- cel- la   ch'in

que- sta E in quel- l'al- tr'on- da Ur- tan-

- do,   ur- tan- do ur- tan- do và.

Pas- so di pe- na in

pe-   na, di pe-   na in pe- na   Co- me la na- vi-

5

quest'in quel- l'al- tr'on- da Ur- tan-

- do, ur- tan- do, ur- tan- do

và.

Il ciel tuo- na e ba- le- na Il

mar tut- t'è il tem- pe- sta   Por- to non ve- de, ò spon- da,

por- to non ve- de, ò spon- da   Do- ve ap-pro-dar non sà.   Do- ve,

do- ve, do- ve, do- ve ap- pro- dar_____ non sà.

tr   D.C.

D.C.

In qual stra- no, e con-fu- so   vor- ti- ce di pen- sie- ri   la mia

men- te s'ag- gi- ra? O- r'è in cal- ma, or s'a- di- ra, e

do- ve an- cor si fer- mi, non ri- sol- ve. Or in sas- so, or in

pol- ve, vor- ria can- giar- si. Oh Di- o! Mà di che ma- i,

mà di che ti que-rel- li cor in- cre-du- lo, in- fi- do?

Di che ti la - gni, ahi - me! for - se non sa - i che nel se - no di

Clo - ri hai por - to, hai li - do!

Andante

Se à me ri - vol-ge il ci - glio L'a -

-ma- to mi- o te- so- ro, l'a- ma- to mi- o te- so- ro Non

sen- to___ più___ mar- to- ro Mà tor- no à re- spi- rar, _____

à re- spi-

11

à re- spi- rar.

Non

te- me più pe- ri- glio Non sen- te af- fan- no, e pe- na L'al-

-ma e si ras- se- re- na, l'al- -ma e si ras- se- re- na

Co - me__ la__ cal-

tr *tr* *tr* *tr*

tr *tr* *tr* *tr* *tr* *tr*

[3]

tr

ma, la cal- ma in mar, co- me la cal- ma in mar.

D. C.

D. C.

Fonti del pianto

Pian - ge - te tan - to, pian - ge - te tan - to

Si - no che in la -

- gri - me   Strug - ga - si il cor.

Fon - ti___ del___ pian -

- - to   Pian - ge - te tan - to,

[pian- ge - te tan- to]   Si - no che in la -

19

se- gui, el- la ti fug- ge. À duol co- tan- to, se re- sis- ter non

puo- i strug-gi-ti af-flit- to cor strug- gi-ti in pian- to.

Allegro

Guar - da, guar - da nè gl'oc- chi

-do- ro.

Guar- da, guar- da nè gl'oc-chi mie- i Fil- li spie-

-ta- ta oh Dio! oh Dio! [oh Di - o!] Quan- to

cru- del tu se- i Quan- to fe- del son i - o.

55
Guar - da, guar - da quan - to t'a - do -

60
- - - ro, _____ quan - to t'a - do -

65
- ro. Oh Dio! [oh Dio!] Guar - da quan - to cru - del tu

70
se - i Guar - da quan - to fe - del son i - o Guar - da, [guar - da]

quan- to t'a- do - - - - ro, quan-

-to t'a- do- ro.

E co-me è in me l'a-

-mo - re E- qual à tua bel- lez- za Ri- mi- ra en-tro il mio co - re, E-

-qual à tua fie - rez - za, [e - qual à tua fie - rez - za] Il mio mar -

-to - - ro, il mio_____ mar to-

-ro. E - qual à tua fie - rez-za Il mio mar - to- -

- - ro, il mio_____ mar - to- ro.

D.C.

Geme l'onda che parte dal fonte

Ge - me___ l'on - da che par - te___ dal fon - te,

Lan- gue il fio- re, che il so- le non_ve- de, E_in la val- le, nel

pra- to_e su'l mon- te Sem- pre_in pian-

- to o- ra par- te o- ra rie- de U- si-

- gnuol _____ che_ l'a- man- te per- de.

-ge Co- me l'al- ma, cui duo- lo cir- con-

-da, Ca- ro Tir- si, lon- ta- na dà

te. Co- me l'al- ma, cui duo- lo__ cir-

-con- -da, Ca-ro Tir- si, lon- ta- na dà te.

Ah ch'un im-men-sa do- glia tut- ta mi strug-ge in pian-to, e non sò

co- me que- sta, ch'in te sol vi- ve al- ma d'a-mor fe-

-ri- ta Lun-ghe dà gl'oc-chi tu- oi ri- man- ga in vi- ta. Sò ben che se la

speme di ri-tor-nar à va-gheg-giar-ti an-co-ra

non tem-pra neun do-lor co-sì in-hu- ma-no, ciò che non fe-ce il

duol fa-ra la ma- no. Che men fie-ro sa-reb-be, e rio mar-

-ti- re, u-na vol-ta mo-rir, che o-gn'or lan-gui- re.

Allegro

Deh, deh non par-tir si pre - sto Con-

-for - to del mio cor_____ Ri - sto - ro al mio_ pe - nar_____

[3]   [3]

_____ Ca - ra spe - ran- -

-nar, [ri- sto- ro al pe- nar]_____ Ca- - ra spe- ran-

- - za.

Deh non par-tir si pre-sto Con- for- to del mio cor,__ [con- for- to del mio cor__] Ca-

- ra spe- ran- -

-lor___ Che ten-ta d'at-ter- rar_____

___ La mia___ co- stan- - za, la mia co-stan-

-za. Che ten- ta d'at-ter- rar_____

La mia co- stan-za, la mia_____ co- stan - za.

D. C.

D. C.

Par che tardo

Par   che

40

ri- schia- ra.

Par che

tar - do ol - tre jl co - stu - me Og - gi

scen- da al mar d'At - lan - te Il bel _____

Dio che _____ col _____ suo _____ lu - me E la ter -

ra, e il ciel _____ ri - schia -

44

-tan- to il co- re-a- man- te, il co- re-a- man- te, Cui l'oc-ca- so ap-pre-sta un

be- ne Tro-va il duol nel- la sua spe- ne E à sof-frir go- den- do im-

-pa -

- ra, go-den- do im-pa- ra. Tro-va il duol nel- la sua

spe - ne E à sof-frir go- den- do im-pa-

- ra, go- den-do im-pa- ra.

Quan- do tu d'An-fi- tri- te in grem- bo gi- a- ce- rai, ce- le-ste Au-

-ri- ga, io del- la bel- la Clo- ri in grem- bo go- de-

47

Clo-ri De'miei do- lo- ri,de'miei do- lo-ri, ri-sto-ro av-rò,

ri- sto- ro av- rò.

Al- l'or_____ ch'in cie- lo

Not- -te il suo ve- lo di- sten- de-

-rà._____ In brac- cio à Clo- ri De' miei do- lo- ri, de' miei do- lo- ri, ri-sto- ro av-

-rò, _____

_____ ri- sto- ro av- rò. _____ Al- l'or ch'in _____ cie- lo Not -

- te il ve- lo _____ di- sten- de- rà. De' miei do-

-sto-   ro, ri- sto- ro av- rò.

De' scor- si af- fan-   ni

A- mor i dan- ni com- pen- se- rà   E la mia

fe - de Dol - ce mer - ce - de, dol - ce mer - ce -

- - de ri - tro - ve - rò. Dol - ce mer -

-ce - - - -

- - - de ri - tro - ve - rò.

tr *tr*

D.C.

D.C.

Sorge vermiglia in ciel

Sor-ge ver-mi-glia in ciel la bel-la Au-ro-ra, ed io do-len-te al-l'o- ra per

cru-del- tà d'a- mor di pe-na in pe- na mi vò strug-gen-do, oh Di- o, sen- za spe-rar pie-

-tà del do-lor mi- o. Quan-do tra l'om- bre poi E- spe-ro

lu - ce   rad-dop-piar-mi al-lor sen-to   il mio fie- ro tor- men- to;   E co - sì pas-so

sem-pre i gior-ni,   e l'o-re,   e quan-do na-sce il sol,   e quan-do muo- re.

Largo

Muo - - re il so - le, E al - lor io sen - to un tor-men-to Che nel

se - no il cor vien me - no, Se non hà di me pie - tà.

Muo - - re il so - le, E al - lor,____

_e al- lor io sen- to un tor- men- to Che nel se- no_il cor vien

me- no, Se_ non_hà di_ me pie- tà,_____ di_ me pie- tà.

Ah, Sil- via, tu sei quel- la cru- de- le Pa- sto- rel- la, che sa- zia_an-cor non

sei di tor-men-tar- mi. Se_à pa- sce- re l'ar- men- to io ti ri-

-tro- vo il mio di- let- to e- gl'è di ri- mi- rar- ti; Mà quan- do al- la ca- pan- na fai ri-

-tor- no per- do tut- to il pia- cer di va- gheg- giar- ti. Se ti

se- guo, mi fug- gi, se ti par- lo d'a- mor, fie- ra e spie-

-ta- ta, mi scher- ni- sci, e m'of- fen- di, e la pa- ce al mio cor vie- ti e con- ten- di.

Mà se sa-pes-si al-me- no, co- me pla-ca-re un di la tua fie- rez- za! Oh Dio! che pos-so

sol nel mio mar- ti- re, a- mar-ti col spe-ra- re, e col sof-fri- re.

Allegro

Ar- di, sve- na, im- pia- ga, at-

-ter- ra Si - no il ciel, i Dei, la ter - ra Sve-

glia pur con- tro di_ me,___ sve - glia__

pur con-tro di me.

Ar - di, sve - na, im - pia - ga, at - ter - ra Si - no il ciel, i

Dei, la ter - ra Sve -

glia__ pur con - tro__ di__ me.

Ar -

- di, sve - na, ar - di,

sve - na, im - pia - ga, at - ter - ra Si - no il ciel, i

Dei, la ter - ra Sve -

- - glia___

pur con - tro___ di___ me. Ar - di,___ sve - na im - pia - ga at - ter - ra Si - no il

ciel, i Dei, la ter - ra Sve - glia pur con-tro di me, con- tro di me.

Con mar -

-tir, pe - na, e do - lo - re l'o - dio,

L'i - ra, e'l tuo ri - go - re sa- zia pu - re,

All'ombra di sospetto

Al-l'om-bra di so - spet-to il mio co-stan-te, af - fet - to per-de al-quan-to la

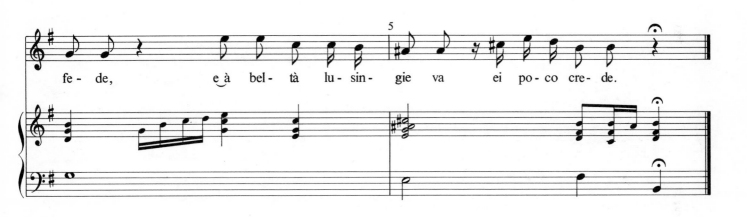

fe - de, e à bel - tà lu - sin - gie va ei po - co cre - de.

Larghetto

[Flute]

[Voice]

Con fin-ti vez - zi.

A - vez - zo non è il

co - re A - mar bel - tà d'a - mo - re Ch'ad - dol - ci - sca il pe -

-nar, ch'ad-dol-ci- sca il__ pe- nar Con fin-ti vez-

-zi. Con

74

Se lu - sin - gie - ro è il dar - do O - gni pia - cer è

tar - do À fia che l'a - do - rar

Per for- za sprez - zi.

À fia che l'a- do- rar

Per for - - za sprez- zi.

Ò quan-ti a-man-ti, ò quan-ti che fe-de-li e co-stan-ti re-gon de-lu-si

dà lu-sin-ghe ac-cor-te d'a-mor frà le ri-tor-te. Più d'o-gni un co-sì lan-gue, e

tan-te vol-te il san-gue spar-ge-ria per mo-strar il ve-ro a-mo-re. Con-cet-to dal-l'ar-

-do-re di vez-zo-sa bel-lez-za ch'o-gn'or gli strug-ge l'al-ma ed al suo af-fet-to

cal - ma   mai spe - ra di go - der,   sin ch'in - gan - na - to

vie - ne a - man - te scher - ni - to,   e in - gan - na - to.

Allegro

[Flute]

[Voice]

Men- ti- ti con- ten- ti ___ Son ve- ri tor- men- ti D'a-

-man- - - te fe- del.

Men- ti- ti con- ten- ti Son

ve- ri tor- men- ti D'a- man-

80

Gran

ma - le è qual be - ne Son dar - di quei guar - di, Che vi - bran_ per_

pe -

- - - -

- - ne Bel- lez- za cru- del.

Che vi - bran_per_ pe - ne Bel- lez- za cru- del.

D.C.

D.C.

D.C.

Lungi dal vago volto

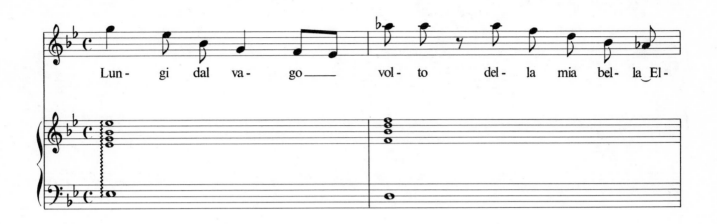

Lun - gi dal va - go _____ vol - to del - la mia bel - la El -

-vi - ra vi - ver non pos - so, vi - ver non pos - so. Oh Di - o! oh

Di - o! e pur cru - do de - stin per mio tor-men - to or mi con - dan - na à pa-sco-lar l'ar -

-men- to,   mà   qual da   lun-ghi am-mi- ra   non di -stin- ta bel-ta- de   il guar-do

mi-   o   Pa- sto- rel- la che vie- ne?   Te- mo d'er-   rar,   mi per- do

cor-   ro,   iv' fer- mo ri- do, e so- spi- ro   ad un

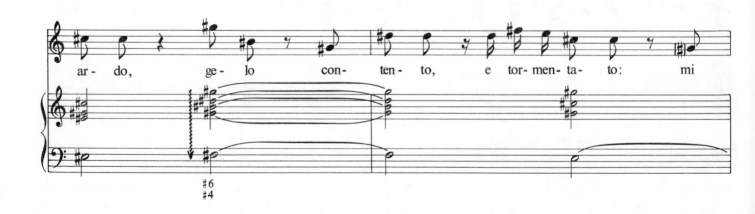

ar-   do,   ge- lo   con- ten- to,   e tor- men- ta- to: mi

Au-gel-let- ti___ voi col

can- to   Que-ste sel- ve im-pre- tio- si- te.   Ed io pos-so___ sol col___

- to Que-ste sel - ve im - pre - tio - si - te.

Au - gel - let - ti voi col can -

- to Que-ste sel - ve im - pre - tio -

-si- te.

Ed io pos- so sol col

pian- to, sol col pian- to__ Con- so- la-

-re, con- so- la- re il mio do-

-lor.

Ed io pos - so— sol col pian - to,— sol col pian-to Con-so-

-la -

-

-

re il mio— do - lor.

Fa- te_ voi che_dol-ce in-can- to Con a-

-mor ò___ con pie- ta- de e Chia- mi al bo-sco il mio te- sor, chia- mi al

bo- sco il mio te- sor, chia- mi al bo- sco il mio te- sor.

Fa- te

voi che_ dol- ce_in- can- to Con a- mor_ ò_ con pie- ta- de_e Chia- mi al

bo-

_ _ sco il mio te-

-sor. Chia - mi al bo - sco il mio te - sor, chia - mi al bo - sco il mio te - sor.

D.C.

Al - le - grez-za mio co - re ch'al fin giun-se al-la me - ta l'a - vi-da mia pu - pil - la

94

ti ri-co-nos-co ò bel-la   ti ri- veg-gio mio be-ne   l'ab-brac-cio Pa-sto-rel-la.

Per-do-na ò ca-ra   à   miei so- spe-si af-fet-ti   per-che er-ran- te Pa-stor ve- der non

suo-le   tra que-ste om-bro-se   fron-di   a-per-to   il   so- le.

Allegro

[Violin]

[Voice]

Mi strin- ge-
-rai_ sì,_ sì, Non par- ti- rai_ più_ nò.
Bel- la ti ra- pi- rò Se il cor non ce - - -

sì, Non par - ti - rai__ nò,__ nò. Mi strin - ge - rai sì, sì,__

__ mi strin-ge- rai Non par - ti - rai nò, nò,_____ non par-ti - rai.

Bel- la _____ ti ra- pi- rò, _____ ti ra - pi - rò _____

Se il cor non ce - - -

- de, non ce - de. Sì, sì, sì.

Sì, sì, sì, mi strin - ge - rai, Nò, nò,

nò.   Nò, nò, nò,   non par - ti - rai   Se il

cor___ non___ ce -   -   - de, non ce-

-de.

Av - vin-to al tuo bel sen Ti giu - ro a - ma - to ben, ti

giu - ro a-ma - to ben Che mai ti man-che - rò, che mai ti man-che-

-rò D'a - mor, e fe -

Vengo à voi luci adorate

-tor-no à a- do- rar-

vi, à a-do-rar-   vi.

- vi. Io ri-tor-no lu-ci a-do - ra-te À a - do - rar - vi.

Ben-che sia- te tan-to in-gra- te Ca- re lu- ci del mio be - ne Io la-

Por-tan-do in sen l'ar- dor, che m'ac- cen-de-ste un gior-no i - do- la- tra fe-

-del à voi ri- tor- no. Mà se fos- te pie-to- so ri-

-sto-ro voi non da-te al mio gran fo- co da- te-mi al-men la mor- te per-che trop-po in-sof-

-fri- bi- le mar-ti- re vi- ver nel fo- co è non po-ter mo- ri- re.

-na- re sen-za spe - ran-za È un gran tor - men- -

- to oc-chi ti - ran - -

ni,— oc-chi ti-ran- ni.

Sem- pre pe- na-

-re sen-za spe-ran-za, [sen- za_____ spe- ran- za,] sen-za spe-ran-za È un

gran_ tor- men- - -

to, è un gran tor - men -

119

val ___ spe - ra - re dal - la ___ co - stan - za Un sol mo- men-to in

tan-ti   in af-   fa-ni, in   tan-ti af-fa-   ni.   Un   sol___   mo-   men-   to in

tan-   ti af-fa-   -   -   ni, in   tan-ti af-fa-   ni.